AMERICAN FOLK SONGS

For The Family

VOLUME ONE

by WALTER TRAGERT

Dedicated to William E. Tragert

First off, I'd like to thank my dear friends and family for lightening my load and sharing this road. It's a joy to share this sometimes bumpy ride with talented and caring folks.

This particular musical adventure would not have come to light without the generous support of these fine humans:

Marty Parker, Connor Buchanan, Lew Card, Evie & Julian Wallfisch, Landon & Weston Zahner, David Mountain, Max & Mabel Tompkins, Leigh Stein, Heather Jank, Sidhya Jayakumar, Ada Stehl, Erin Daniels, Maggie Bettner, Emily Barlow, Sarah Thomas, Christy Gray Udall, Allison Cook, The Koehlers, George Ney, The Pollard Boys, Jennifer Cheskiewicz, Katie Simon, Linda Bourianoff, Kazmira Pedonesi, Arron Hester, Amy Baer, Kaila Wyllys & Hugh Winkler, Lynn Goode, Kathy Bolstorff, Jody Klopp, Adam Trotter, Nidhi Nakra

Big thanks to Shelley Yates McNair and Lori Armendariz for their lovely artwork.

Special thanks to Nevie and Annie, Aleks and Ben, and Karen and Tomas.

Most importantly, I must thank the thousands of children who've allowed me to share their musical journey. You (ok, your parents too) have truly been my inspiration over the last twelve years. ¡Muchas gracias!

Thanks for singing me to sleep, Dad!

TABLE of CONTENTS

On rainy days as a child, I used to lay on the floor flipping through the dusty old books my parents kept stashed on shelves in every room. One afternoon, I came across a book called *The Fireside Book of Folksongs*. It was filled with music from all over the world. Each page was a work of art, including luminous drawings and rich stories about each song. Even though much of the music was new to me, I was immediately drawn in. I couldn't put the book down!

Many years later, I began work on this project. While finishing up the recording element, a package came in the mail from my dad: it was *The Fireside*! That was the moment that I realized I wanted to make a songbook to accompany the record.

FUN FACT

My house has wheels. That's right - I live in a 27 ft. travel trailer. When I moved here in 2015, there was a small 4′ x 6′ bedroom in the back. In short order, I turned it into a tiny recording studio, and I'm proud to say that every track on this collection was recorded between those humble walls. My studio may not big enough to stand up in, but there's more than enough space to make musical magic.

JOHN the RABBIT

Traditional / Arranged by Walter Tragert

As a teen, I loved playing around with my friend's banjo. It wasn't until I was almost 50 that I finally got my own, and taught myself to play. With a banjo back in my hands, I was instantly reconnected with the folk music of my youth, which inspired me to make this recording project. *John the Rabbit* is a long-time favorite of mine.

Oh, John The Rabbit (yes m'am!)
Got a mighty habit
Jumpin' in my garden
Cuttin' down my cabbage
My sweet potatoes
My fresh tomatoes
And if I live
To see next fall
I ain't gonna have
No garden at all
No m'am

A traditional African-American call and response song from the 1800's.

Walter Daniels – harmonica   Scrappy Jud Newcomb – slide guitar
Walter – voices, banjo, guitar

3

STEALIN'

Written by Will Shade / Additional lyrics by Walter Tragert

My friend Erik taught me to play this song when I was around twelve years old. He and his dad were both musical, and introduced me to a ton of classic folk songs. Looking back, I think my best memories of learning music took place when I played with a friend - like Erik. If you're feeling inspired, go find yourself a music buddy and learn to play!

Stealin', stealin'
Pretty mama don't you tell on me
'Cause I'm stealing' back
To my same ole used to be

Put your arms around me
Like a circle 'round the sun
You know I'll love you honey
When my easy ridin's done

You don't believe I love you
Look at the fool I've been
You don't believe I'm sinkin'
Look at the hole I'm in

The girl I love
She's long and tall
She sleeps in the kitchen
With her feet out in the hall

You don't believe I love you
Look at the fool I've been
You don't believe I'm sinkin'
Look at the hole I'm in

Written by Will while he was part of The Memphis Jug Band.

Stanley Smith - clarinet   Scrappy - mandolin
Walter - voices, banjo, guitar, bugle, trumpet, trombone, baritone horn

Oh SUSANNAH

Written by Stephen Foster

One of my earliest memories is singing this song in Mrs. Koch's kindergarten class. There was a girl in our class was named Amy, and she knew all the words to all the verses. I still remember thinking that was pretty cool.

Well I come from Alabama with a banjo on my knee
Goin' to Louisiana, my true love for to see

Oh Susannah, oh don't you cry for me
Cause I come from Alabama with a banjo on my knee

Well it rained all night the day I left, the weather it was dry
The sun so hot I froze to death, Susannah don't you cry

Well I had a dream the other night, the weather it was still
Saw my ole Susannah a-comin' down the hill
A buckwheat cake was in her mouth, a tear was in her eye
Says I, "Am comin' from the south, Susannah don't you cry."

Well I come from Alabama with a banjo on my knee
Goin' to Louisiana, my true love for to see

Written by Stephen Foster, one of America's first professional songwriters.

Peter Stiles - mandolin   Phil Davidson - fiddle
Walter - voices, banjo, guitar, spoons

I'VE BEEN WORKIN' ON the RAILROAD

Traditional / Arranged by Walter Tragert

My dad always sang this song to me at bedtime. The first go 'round would end, and I'd beg "Again, Daddy!" By the end of the second round, my eyes would flutter closed, and my dad would tuck me in and start to leave. Before he'd get to the door, I'd snap awake and beg once more: "Again, Daddy!" He'd start his third round, but before the third verse was over, I was in a peaceful sleep, dreaming of trains.

I've been workin' on the railroad
All the live long day
I've been working' on the railroad
Just to pass the time away
Can't ya hear the whistle blowin'
Rise up so early in the morn
Can't ya hear the captain shouting
"Dinah, blow your horn!"

Dinah won't ya blow, Dinah won't ya blow
Dinah won't ya blow your horn
Dinah won't ya blow, Dinah won't ya blow
Dinah won't ya blow your horn

Someone's in the kitchen with Dinah
Someone's in the kitchen I know
Someone's in the kitchen with Dinah
Strummin' on the ole banjo (keep singing')

Fee, fi, fiddly-i-o, Fee, fi, fiddly-i-o
Fee, fi, fiddly-i-o, Strummin' on the ole banjo

First published as "The Levee Song" in 1894.
It is likely a combination of several earlier songs.

Walter Daniels - harmonica   Walter - voices, banjo, guitar, horse (coconuts!)

SHE'LL BE COMIN' AROUND *the* MOUNTAIN

Traditional / Arranged by Walter Tragert

Long car trips were a big part of my childhood, and this song was one of my family's favorite road trip songs. Sometimes, we'd make up our own verses that got sillier as time went on: "She'll be wearing stinky socks when she comes - peee-yew!"

She'll be comin' 'round the mountain when she comes (toot! toot!)
She'll be comin' 'round the mountain when she comes (toot! toot!)
She'll be coming' 'round the mountain, she'll be coming' 'round the mountain
She'll be comin' 'round the mountain when she comes (toot! toot!)

She'll be drivin' six white horses when she comes (whoa back!)
She'll be drivin' six white horses when she comes (whoa back!)
She'll be drivin' six white horses, she'll be drivin' six white horses
She'll be drivin' six white horses when she comes (whoa back!)

And we'll all go out to meet her when she comes (Hi, babe!)
Yes we'll all go out to meet her when she comes (Hi, babe!)
Yes we'll all go out to meet her, yes we'll all go out to meet her
Yes we'll all go out to meet her when she comes (Hi, babe!)

And we'll all have chicken and dumplings when she comes (yum! yum!)
Yes we'll all have chicken and dumplings when she comes (yum! yum!)
Yes we'll all have chicken and dumplings, yes we'll all have chicken and dumplings
Yes we'll all have chicken and dumplings when she comes (yum! yum!)

She'll be comin' 'round the mountain when she comes (clap your hands!)
She'll be comin' 'round the mountain when she comes
She'll be coming' 'round the mountain, she'll be coming' 'round the mountain
She'll be comin' 'round the mountain when she comes

Additional verse: (Make up your own!)

And we'll all get very sleepy when she comes
Yes we'll all get very sleepy when she comes
Yes we'll all get very sleepy, yes we'll all get very sleepy
Yes we'll all get very sleepy when she comes.............zzzzzzzzzz

The first printed version of this song appeared in Carl Sandburg's "The American Songbag" in 1927. It is believed to have originated during the late 1800's, based on an old spiritual titled "When the Chariot Comes."

Walter - voice, banjo

11

SKIP To MY LOU

Traditional / Arranged by Walter Tragert

As a preschooler, I went to a neighborhood nursery school. The teacher, Mrs. Collins, gave us report cards with grades on subjects like "listening," "sharing," etc. My worst subject was "skipping," in which I got an F - with a note in the margin saying "he happily tries." Looking back, this note reflects my approach to everything in life! PS - I eventually did figure out how to skip!

Lost my partner, what'll I do?
Lost my partner, what'll I do?
Lost my partner, what'll I do?
Skip to my lou, my darlin'

Skip, skip, skip to my lou
Skip, skip, skip to my lou
Skip, skip, skip to my lou
Skip to my lou, my darlin'

Flies in the buttermilk, shoo fly shoo!
Flies in the buttermilk, shoo fly shoo!
Flies in the buttermilk, shoo fly shoo!
Skip to my lou, my darlin'

Little red wagon painted blue
Little red wagon painted blue
Little red wagon painted blue
Skip to my lou, my darlin'

Lost my partner, what'll I do?
Lost my partner, what'll I do?
Lost my partner, what'll I do?
Skip to my lou, my darlin'

Find me another one, maybe two!
Find me another one, maybe two!
Find me another one, maybe two!
Skip to my lou, my darlin'

"Skip to My Lou" was a popular American partner-stealing dance from the 1840's. The song was often used in "play parties" Look it up!

Peter Stiles - mandolin   Phil Davidson - fiddle   Landis Armstrong - guitar   Walter - voices, banjo, guitar

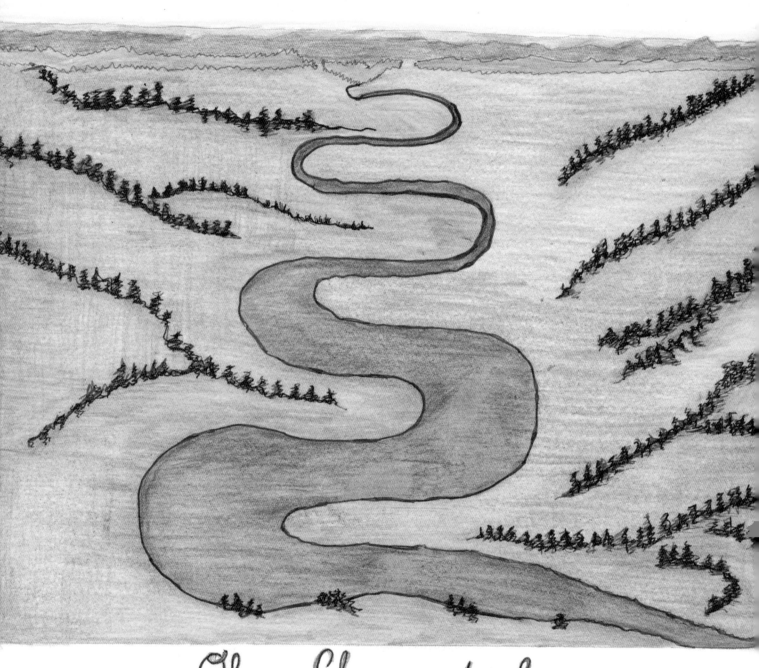

Oh, Shenandoah

Oh SHENANDOAH

Traditional / Additional lyrics by Walter Tragert

I have always loved watching rivers flow. The way they change course over time and how the water you see is entirely different from moment to moment. There are so many verses to this song, it was hard to pick my favorite ones.

Oh Shenandoah I long to see you
Away you rolling river
Oh Shenandoah I long to see you
Away, I'm bound away
'Cross the wide Missouri

Oh Shenandoah I love your daughter
Away you rolling river
For her I'd cross the mighty water
Away, I'm bound away
'Cross the wide Missouri

Oh Shenandoah I'm bound to leave you
Away you rolling river
Oh Shenandoah I'll not deceive you
Away, I'm bound away
'Cross the wide Missouri

A traditional American folk song of uncertain origin, dating to the early 19th century. This capstan shanty might have originated with Canadian and American voyageurs or fur traders traveling down the Missouri River.

Walter – voices, banjo, guitar, bass, harmonica, baritone horn

15

THIS LAND
is
YOUR LAND

Written by Woody Guthrie

I can't remember when I first heard this song but I've always loved it. I saw Pete Seeger perform
it at a folk festival and he had the whole audience singing along. I will never forget that!

This land is your land, this land is my land
From California to the New York islands
From the redwood forests to the gulf stream waters
This land was made for you and me

As I went walking that ribbon of highway
I saw above me that endless skyway
I saw below me that golden valley
This land was made for you and me

Well I roamed and I rambled and I followed my footsteps
To the sparkling sands of her diamond desert
And all around me a voice was sounding
This land was made for you and me

Well the sun was shining and I went strolling
With the wheat fields waving and the dust clouds rolling
And a voice was chanting as the fog was lifting
This land was made for you and me

These lyrics were written by American folk singer Woody Guthrie in
1940 based on an existing tune called "When the World's on Fire."

Walter Daniels - harmonica   Peter Stiles - mandolin
Phil Davidson - fiddle   Walter - voices, banjo, guitar, bass

LIL' LIZA JANE

Traditional / Additional lyrics by Walter Tragert

Liza Jane was always one of my favorite songs to perform in music classes with young kids. A fun fact that you may not know: it's a tradition to make up your own verses based on where you live and the people you know. Go ahead and try it. It's time to rhyme!

I know a girl that you don't know
Lil' Liza Jane
Way down south in Baltimore
Lil' Liza Jane

Oh, Eliza!

Lil' Liza Jane
Oh, Eliza!
Lil' Liza Jane

See that guy all dressed in red
Lil' Liza Jane
Give him five dollars, he'll shave your head
Lil' Liza Jane

See that girl with socks of green
Lil' Liza Jane
Prettiest girl I've ever seen
Lil' Liza Jane

I know a girl that you don't know
Lil' Liza Jane
Way down south in Baltimore
Lil' Liza Jane

This song dates back at least to the 1910's. It is one of the standards of the New Orleans brass band tradition. It has become a standard in traditional jazz, folk music, bluegrass, and even rock and roll.

John Chipman - snare drum   Stephen Belans - percussion   Larry Fulcher - bass
Larisa Montanaro Chipman - voice   Walter - voices, banjo, pennywhistle, trumpet, trombone

THIS LITTLE LIGHT of MINE

Written by Harry Dixon Loes

When I was 22, I was invited to sing at a rally in Washington, DC as part of a musical puppet play called "Dinosaur Rock." After we did our set, a woman came on the stage and started to sing this song - I had never heard it before. When she asked me to join in on guitar, I was so nervous that I didn't know what to do! Halfway through, I figured it out, and things were going smoothly. Then she turned to me and said "Big gospel ending, son!" When the song ended, she gave me a big hug. Her name was Marian Wright Edelman.

This little light of mine, I'm gonna let it shine
This little light of mine, I'm gonna let it shine

This little light of mine, I'm gonna let it shine
Let it shine, Let it shine, Let it shine

Everywhere I go, I'm gonna let it shine
Everywhere I go, I'm gonna let it shine
Everywhere I go, I'm gonna let it shine
Let it shine, Let it shine, Let it shine

In the darkest night, I'm gonna let it shine
In the darkest night, I'm gonna let it shine
In the darkest night, I'm gonna let it shine
Let it shine, Let it shine, Let it shine

This little light of mine, I'm gonna let it shine
This little light of mine, I'm gonna let it shine

This little light of mine, I'm gonna let it shine
Let it shine, Let it shine, Let it shine
Let it shine, Let it shine, Let it shine
Let it shine, Let it shine, Let it shiiiiiiiiiiiiiiiiiiiiine!

A hymn written by HDL in the 1920's. It eventually became a Civil Rights anthem in the 1950's and 1960's.

Phil Davidson - fiddle   Larry Fulcher - bass
Larisa Montanaro Chipman - voice   Walter - voices, banjo, guitar, harmonica

The DONUT SONG

Traditional / Arranged by Walter Tragert

When I was nine, my family moved from a small town in northeast Ohio to
the Maryland suburbs of Washington D.C. That first summer, I saw something
I had never seen: an ice cream truck. I never knew such a magical thing existed!
I was so excited that I rode my bike back home as fast as I could to get some money -
but nobody was home! I looked everywhere for some change, but couldn't find any.
Being the inventive kid that I was, I grabbed my spoons and went back to the
ice cream truck. The other kids were gone and the driver was about to leave.
I said, "Hey Mister, want to hear a song?" He gave me a funny look and said
"OK, I guess." I played my spoons and sang "The Donut Song" and he gave me
two pieces of sour apple bubblegum. It was my first paid performance!

*Well I walked around the corner
And I walked around the block
And I walked right in to a donut shop
And I picked two donuts
Right out of the grease
And I handed the lady a five-cent piece*

*Well she looked at the nickel
And she looked at me
She said, "This nickel's no good to me
There's a hole in the middle
And it goes right through"
Says I, "There's a hole in the donut too*

Thanks for the donut, so long"

So long everybody!

Sung to the tune of "Turkey In The Straw."

Walter - voice, jaw harp, spoons

WALTER

Walter's musical training began as a mere babe, rocking to the rhythm of "Gloria," as interpreted by his adolescent brother's garage band. Since his portentous start, Walter has crafted his own career as an acclaimed songwriter and performer. A veteran of Austin's live music scene, he has recorded and performed with a variety of artists, from Ian McLagan (The Faces, Rolling Stones) to The Tosca String Quartet. In 1988, he joined Grammy nominees Michele Valeri and Ingrid Crepeau as a cast member of their child-oriented show Dinosaur Rock, touring from coast to coast to the delight of thousands of elementary-schoolers. Throughout his career, Walter has toured extensively and internationally - from Italy and Switzerland to Japan, including a leg with his long-time friend and collaborator Scrappy Jud Newcomb. In 2013 and 2014, Walter was honored as Austin Music Ambassador to Austin's sister city Oita, Japan. Walter taught early childhood music at Austin Community Music School from 2005 to 2017, rocking the sandbox with hundreds of Austin's budding musicians.

Walter is self-taught in a number of instruments, including harmonica, spoons, jaw harp, guitar, bugle, trombone, trumpet, baritone horn, saxophone, flute, piano, pennywhistle, banjo, mandolin, and - of course - voice.

For more info please visit *www.waltertragertmusic.com*

The ARTISTS

Shelley Yates McNair lives with her family in Portland, Oregon. The American West is her inspiration. She makes art to bring light to life. She used acrylic paint on metal for the cover picture and acrylic and oil paints on the song pictures.
skyvisualart.com

Lori Armendariz lives in Austin, Texas with her family in a purple house. She loves making sculptures of mermaids. She used colored pencil for her art in this book. Can you pick them out?
loriarmendariz.carbonmade.com

Cover art by SHELLEY YATES McNAIR
Song art by SHELLEY YATES McNAIR and LORI ARMENDARIZ
Walter photo by ALEKS GAJDECZKA, aleks-gajdeczka.com
Design by MATT ESKEY at ANY & ALL MEDIA, INC., Austin, TX
Recorded at THE LONG BOX (4x6 room in my trailer)
Mixed and mastered by RON FLYNT at JUMPING DOG STUDIO, Austin, TX

25

MUSICAL MEMORIES

Do you have any stories about playing or listening to music with your family, your friends, or maybe even a pet? Write them down here!

MUSICAL MEMORIES

Any more?

MUSICAL DREAMS

Which instrument(s) would you like to learn to play? Do you have any favorite songs?

MUSICAL DREAMS

Any more?

MUSICAL PICTURES

Close your eyes and listen to a song. When the song is over, open your eyes and draw what you see.

MUSICAL PICTURES

No peeking!